Handwriting Program for Cursive - Right Handed

contents

Phyllis Bertin   Eileen Perlman

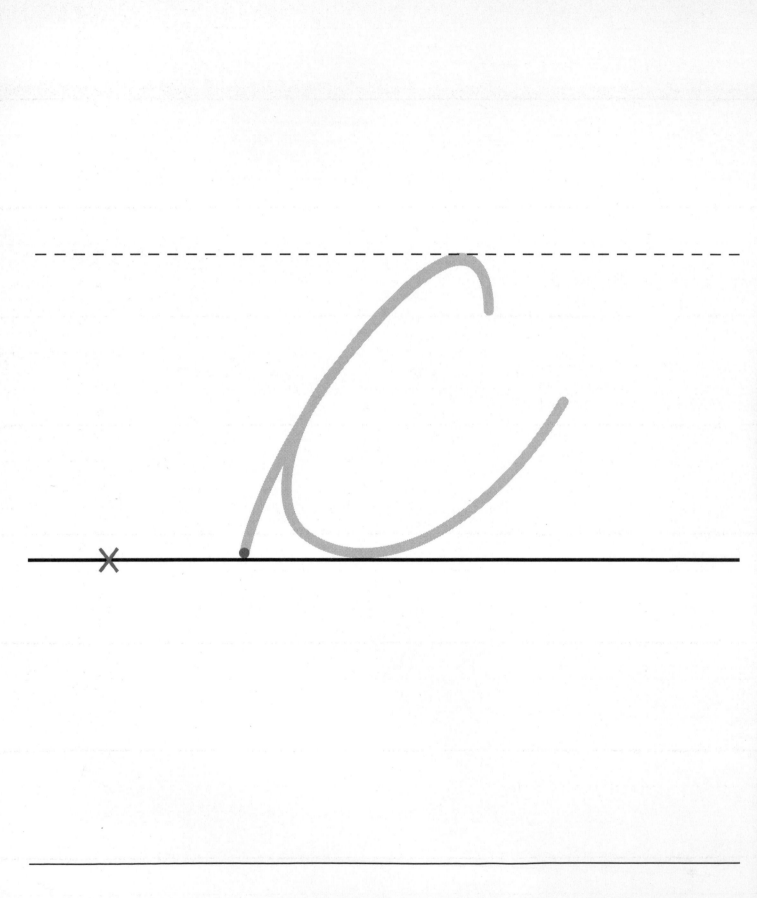

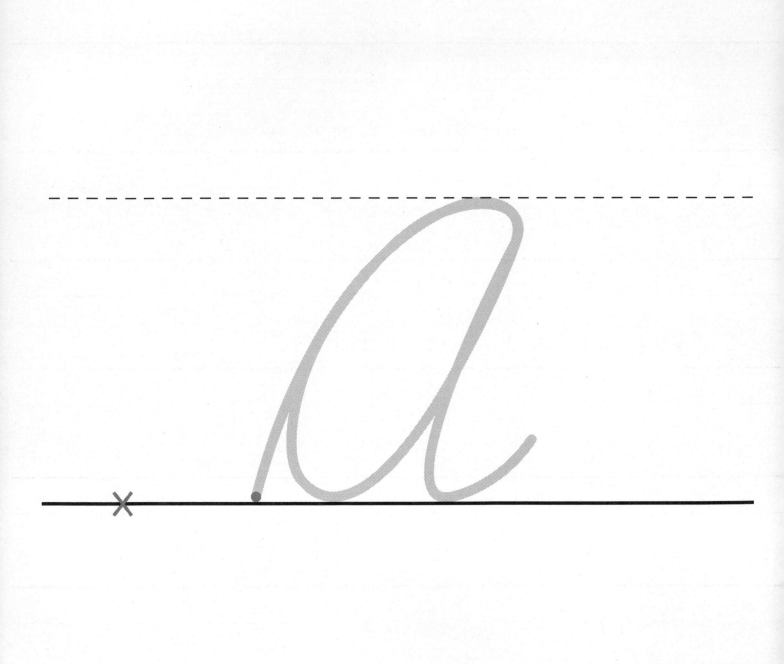

d   d   d   d   d

d   d   d   d   d

da

ad

dad

add

cad

7

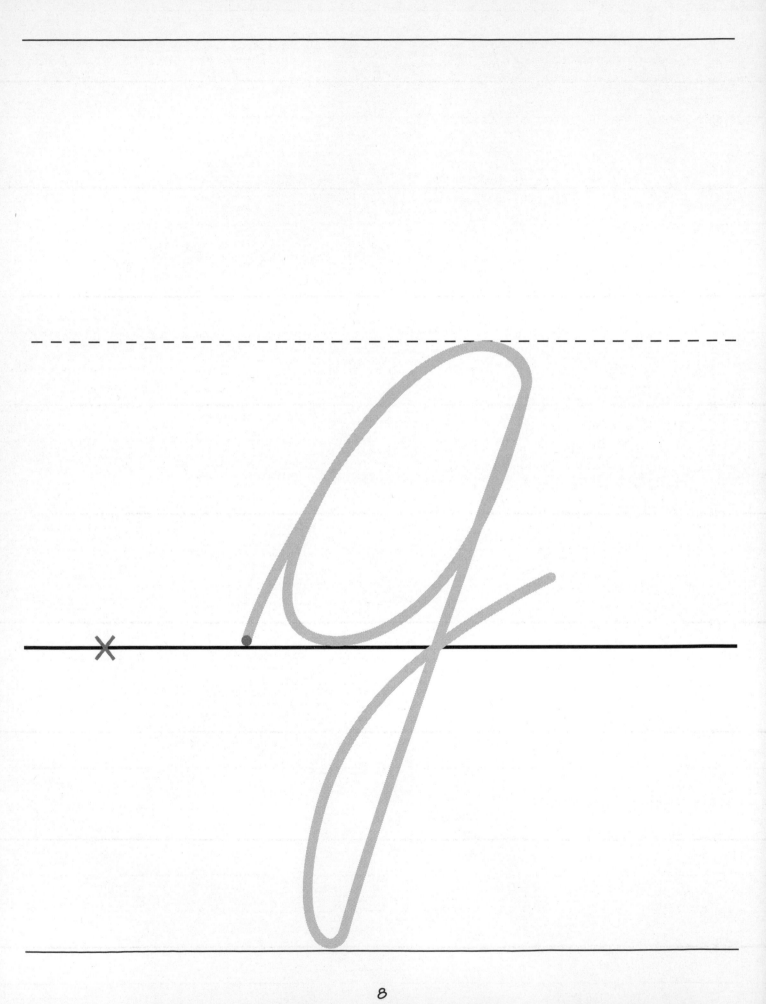

g   *g*   *g*   *g*   *g*

g   *g*   *g*   *g*   *g*

ga

ag

gag

dad

cad

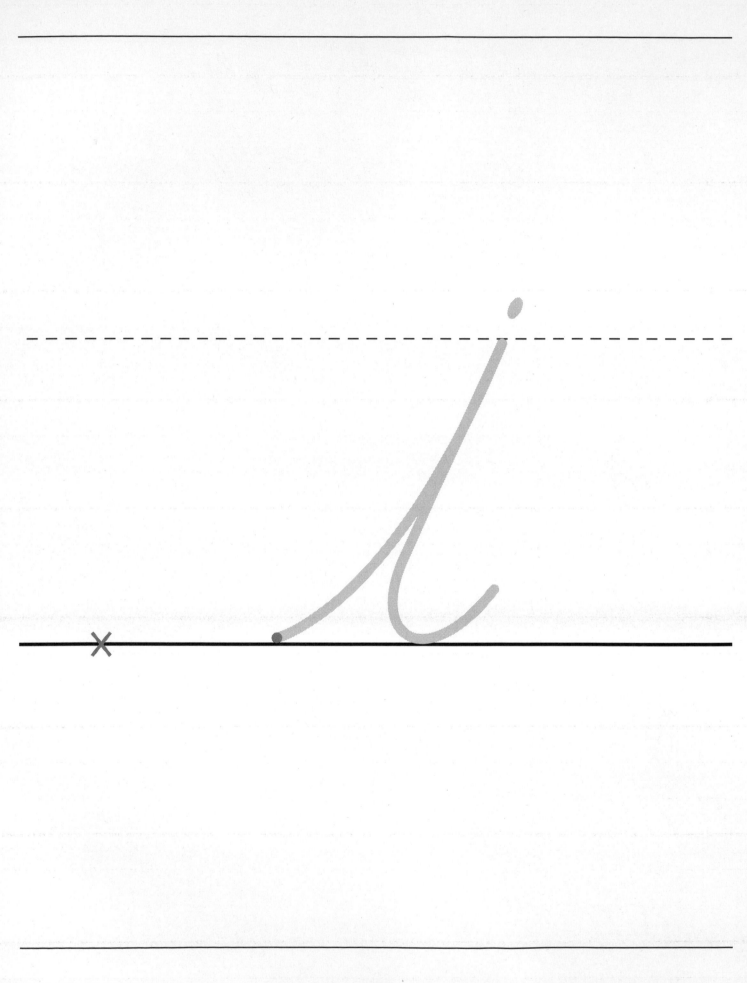

i   *i*   *i*   *i*   *i*

i   *i*   *i*   *i*   *i*

ic

id

ig

ai

di

dig

*u**u**u**u**u*

*u**u**u**u**u*

ud

ug

cu

gu

du

dug

13

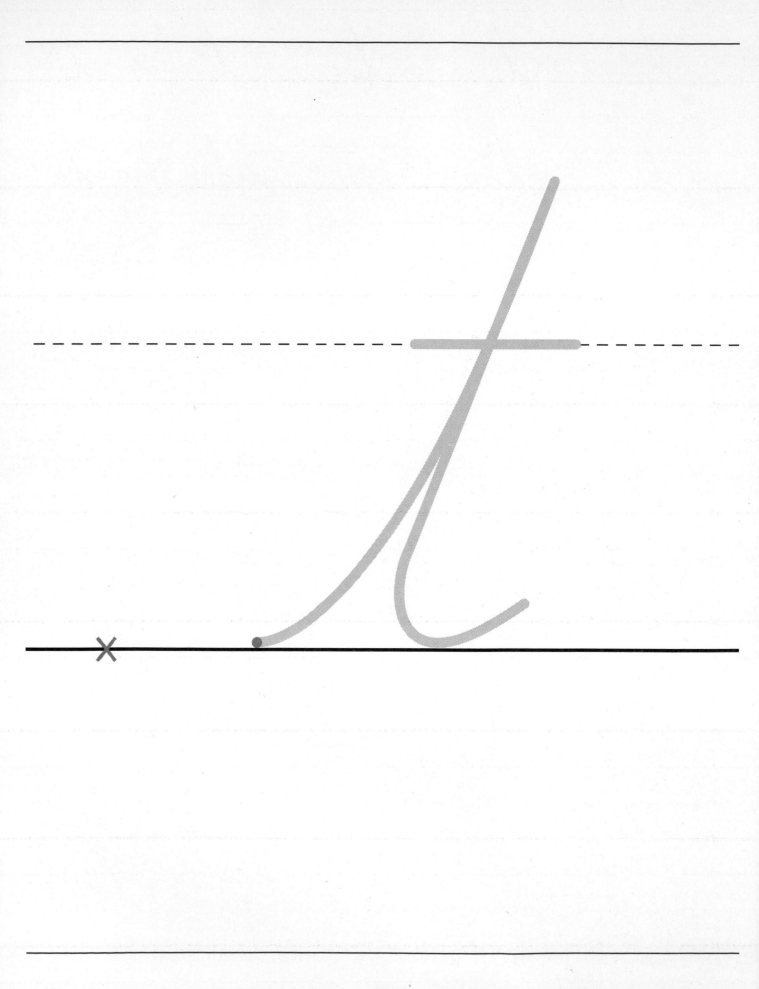

t   t   t   t   t

t   t   t   t   t

at

it

ut

tag

tug

act

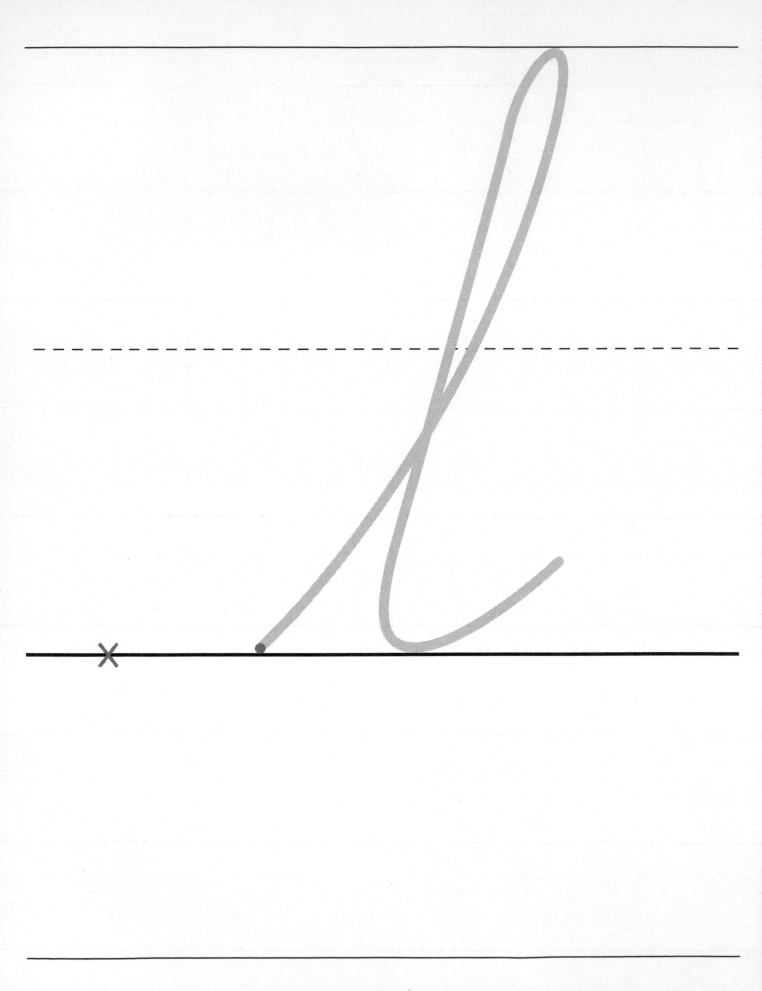

l l l l l

l l l l l

ll ll ll ll

il

la

ul

li

lad

lit

all

tall

ill

dill

gill

dull

c   a

d   g

i   u

t   l

cl

gl

clad

glad

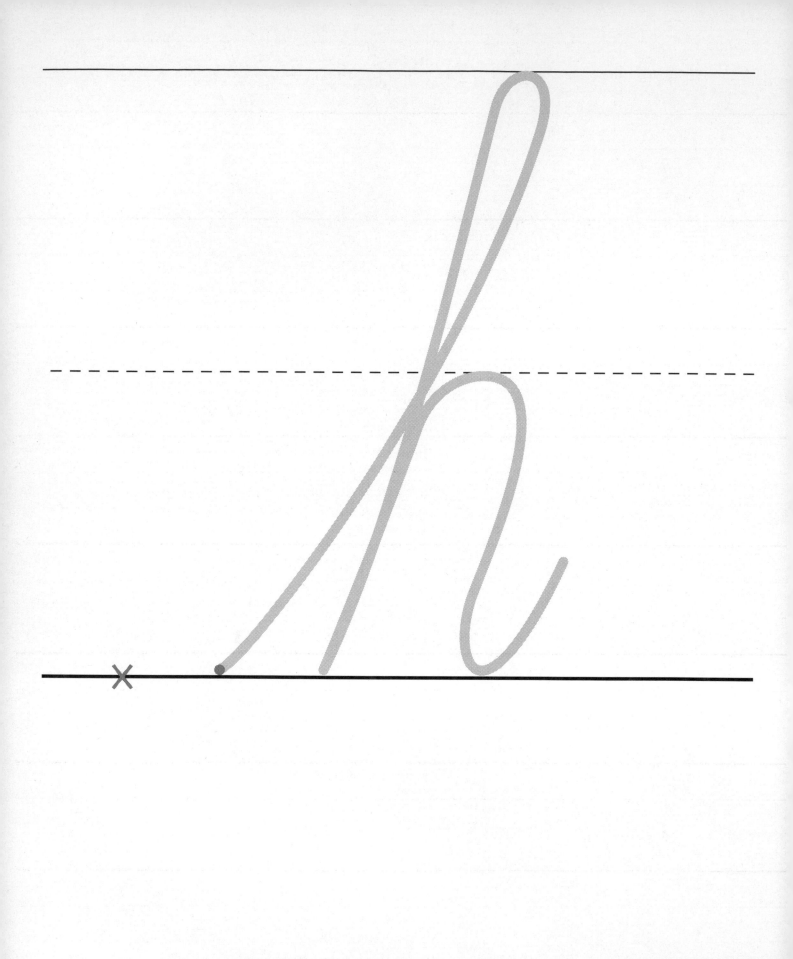

h   h   h   h   h

h   h   h   h   h

ha

hi

hu

ch

hill

chat

21

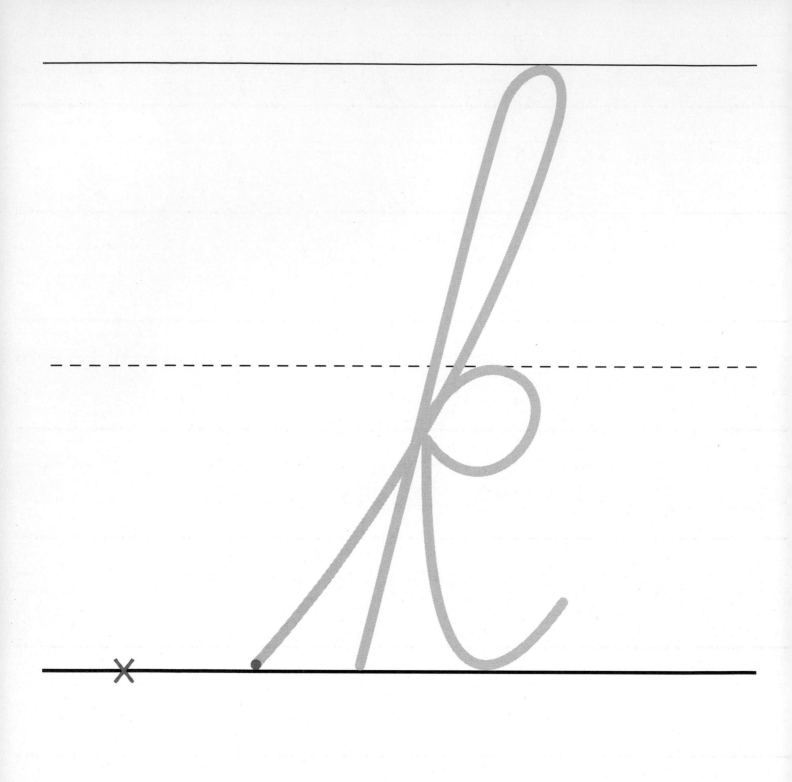

k   k   k   k   k

k   k   k   k   k

ki

kk

ck

kick

tack

lick

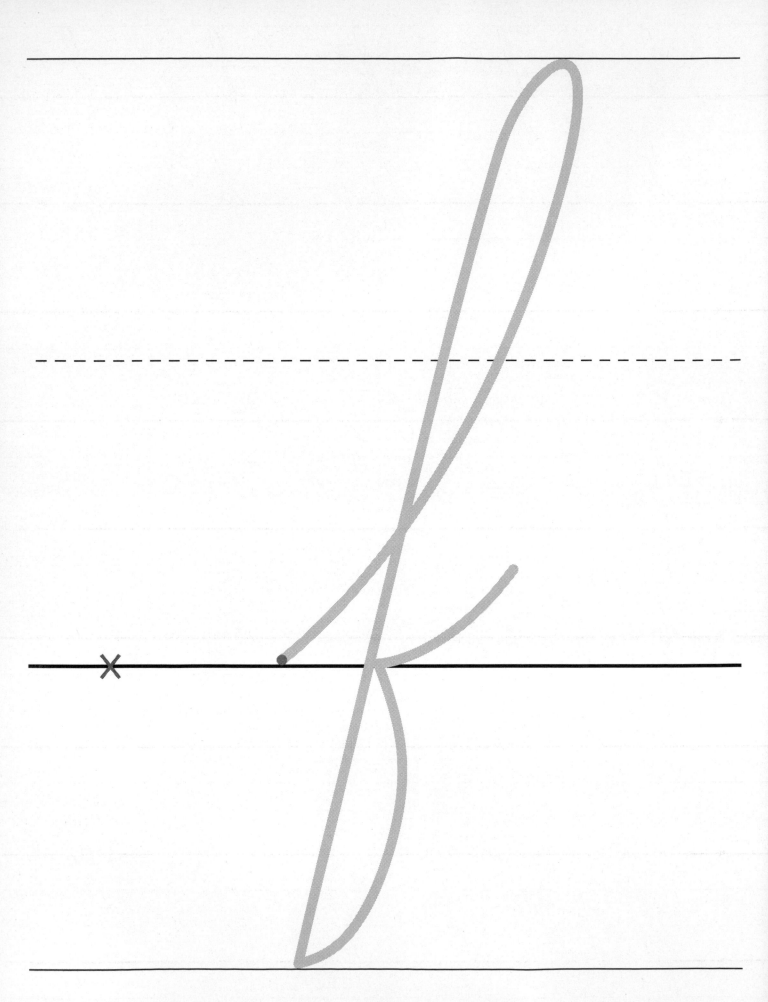

f f f f f

f f f f f

ff

fa

fl

if

cuff

flat

25

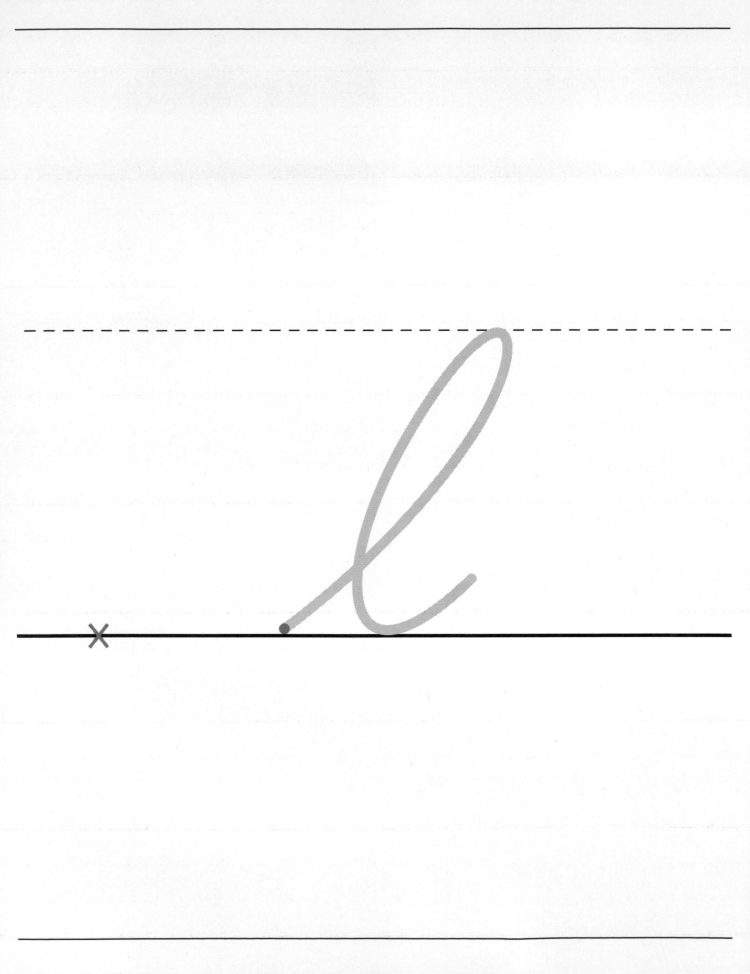

l   l   l   l   l

l   l   l   l   l

ll

la

el

le

fell

felt

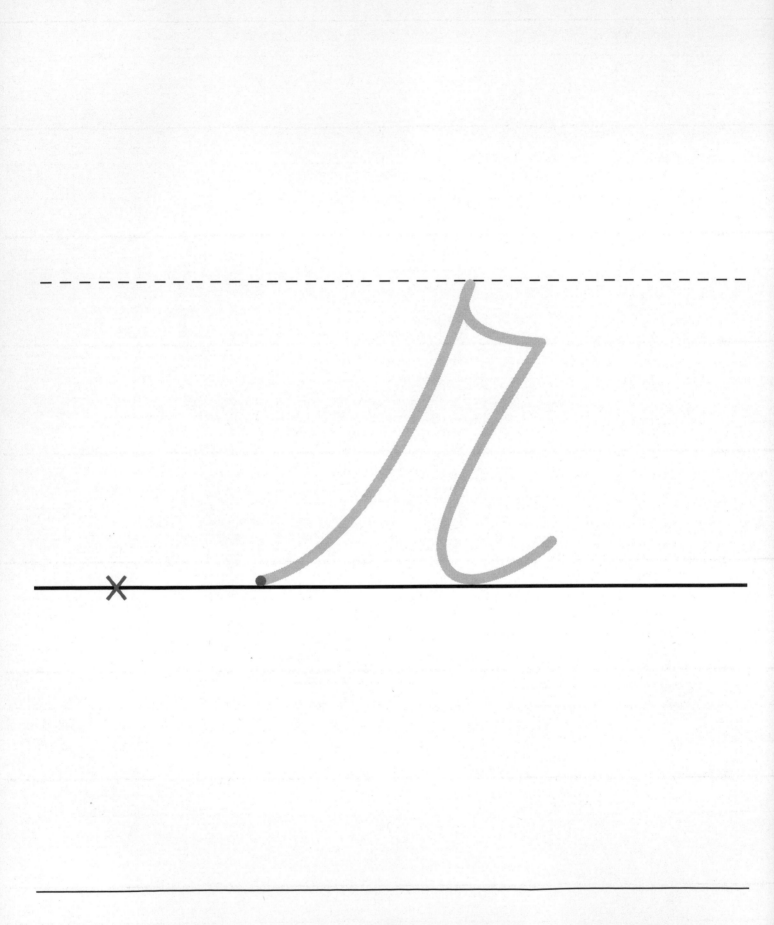

r   *r*   *r*   *r*   *r*

r   *r*   *r*   *r*   *r*

gr

cr

dr

fr

ar

red

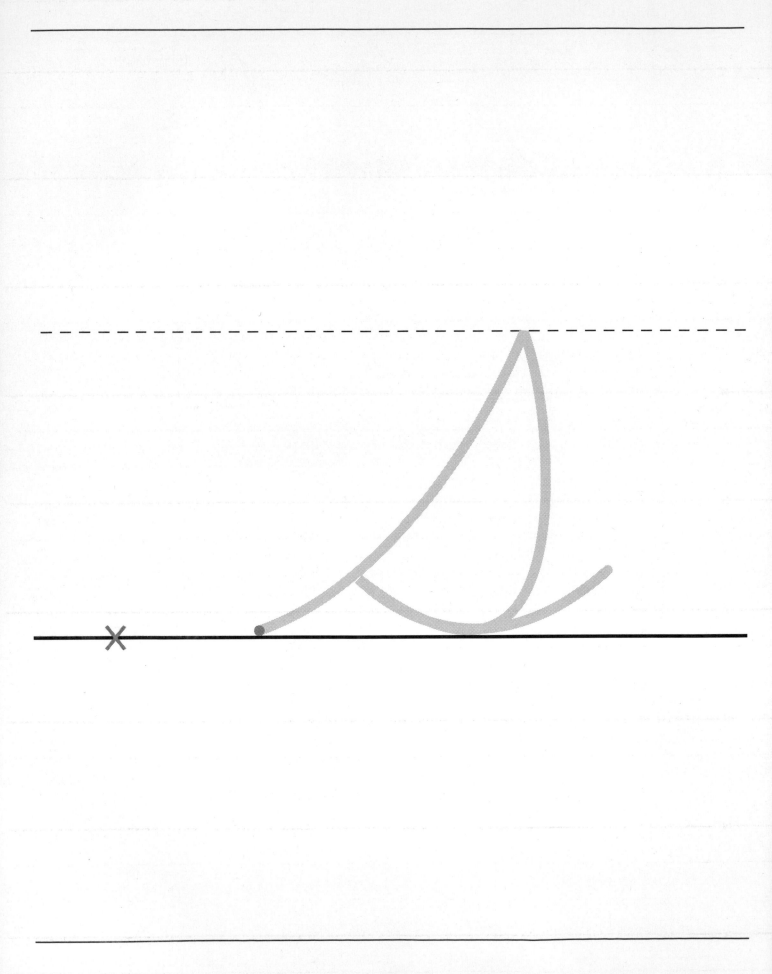

as

is

us

sl

c   a

d   g

i   u

r   s

t   l

l   f

h   k

32

drag

rest

rugs

rust

list

rich

fast

such

kiss

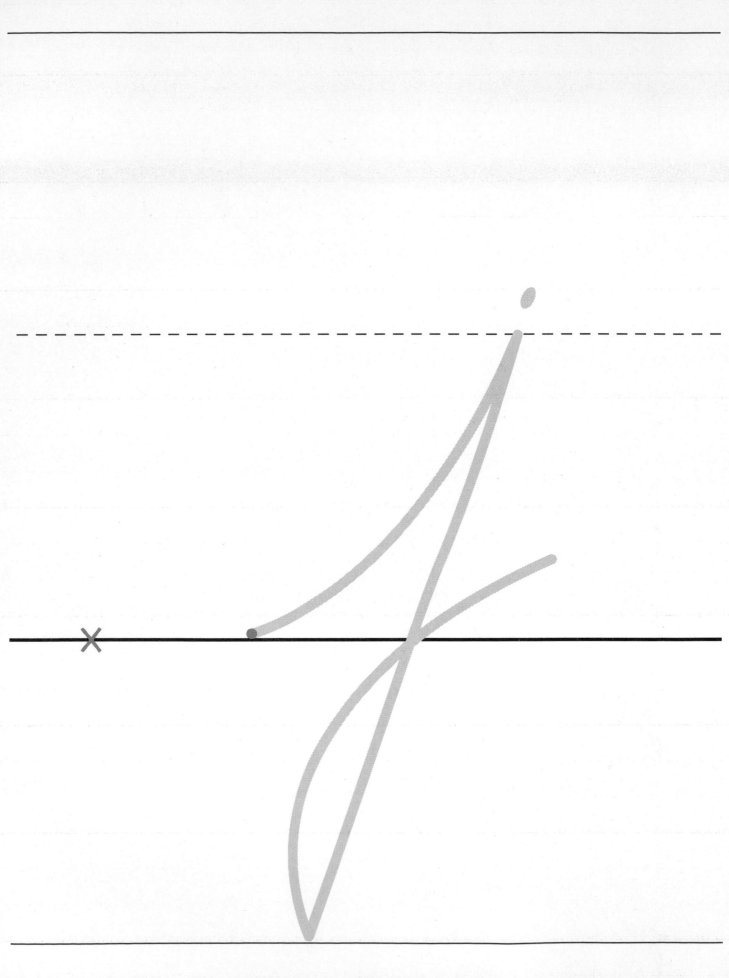

j j j j j

j j j j j

ja

ji

je

ju

jet

jug

p p p p p

p p p p p

pa

pe

pl

up

pr

pups

37

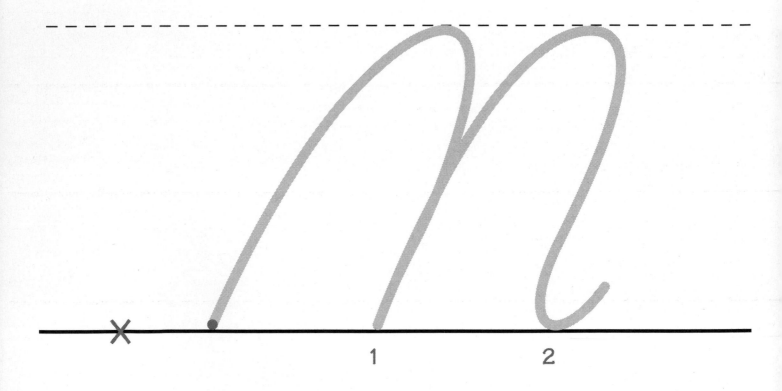

1

2

m m m m m

1   2

m m m m m

an

en

in

un

map

nut

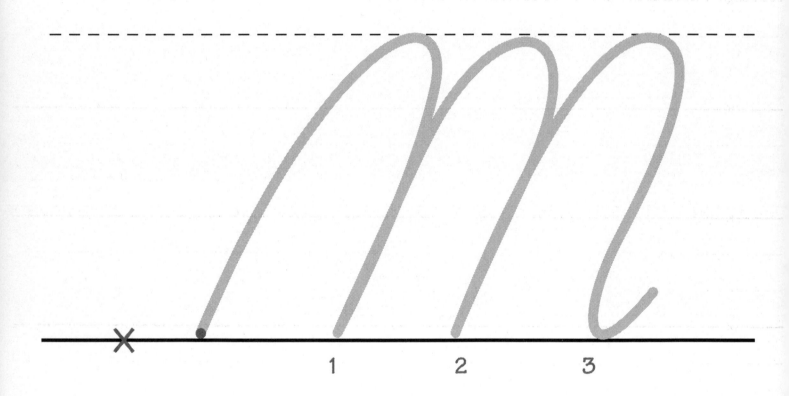

1   2   3

m   m   m   m   m
1 2 3

m   m   m   m   m

me

mu

am

im

jam

maps

m m

1 2   1 2 3

an   am

ni   mi

en   em

nu   mu

men

man

mend

mint

sun

ran

met

mad

jump

plan

must

junk

lamp

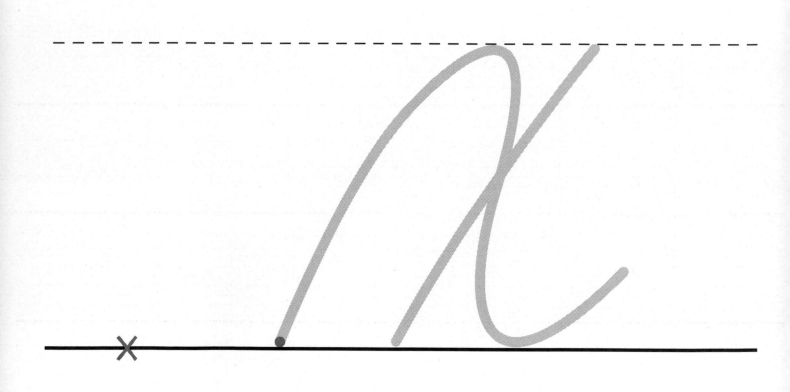

x x x x x

x x x x x

ax

ix

ex

six

mix

exit

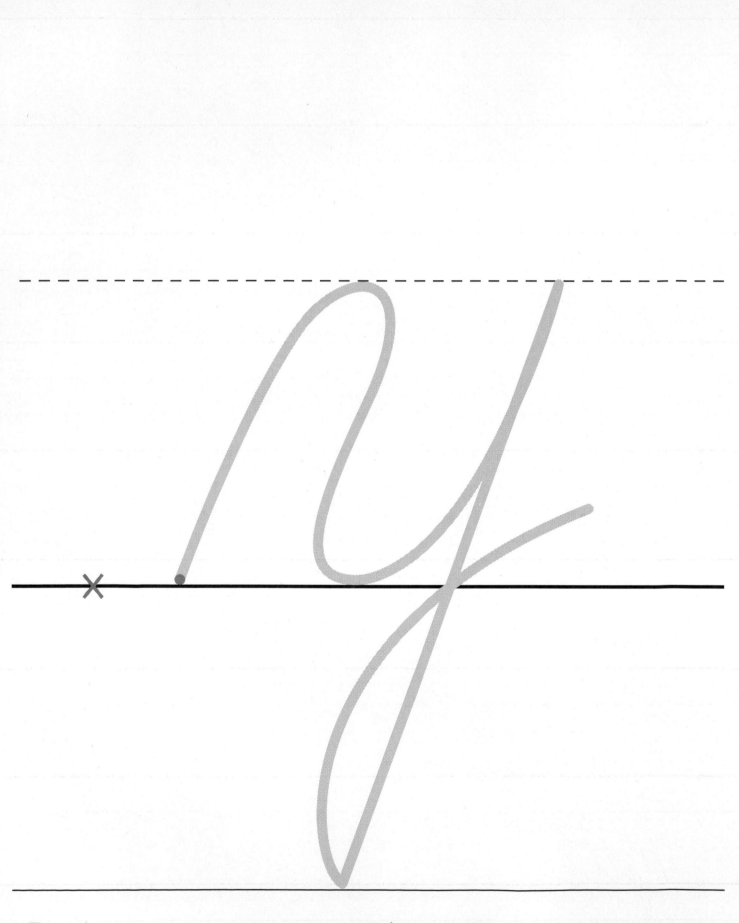

y   *y*   *y*   *y*   *y*

y   *y*   *y*   *y*   *y*

ay

by

ey

yes

yet

yell

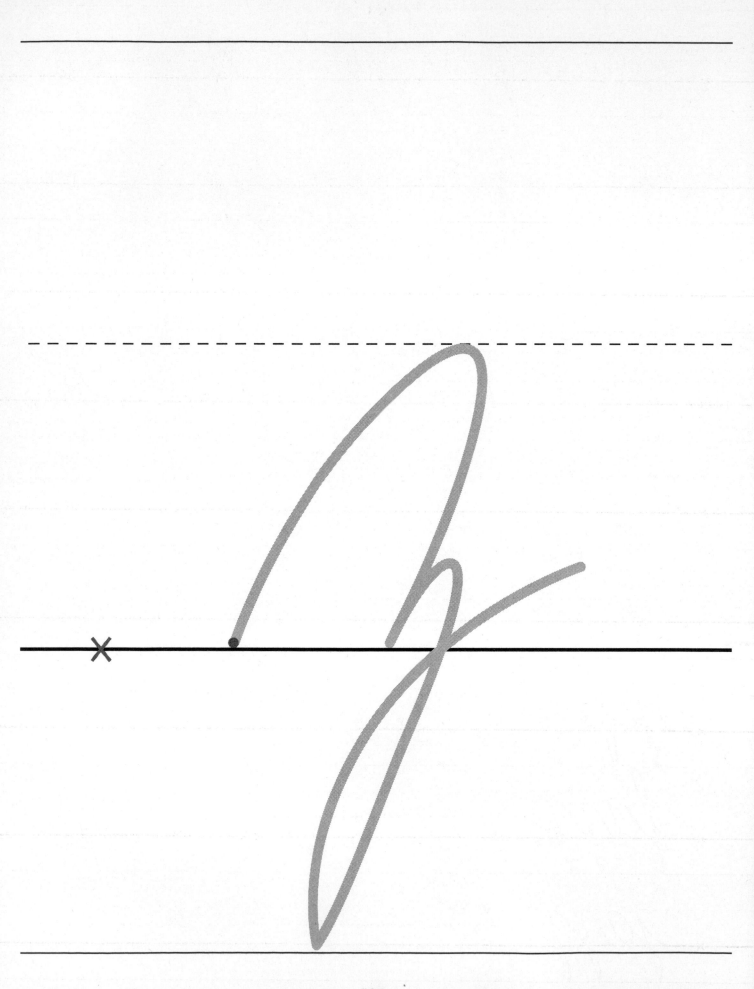

g   *g*   *g*   *g*   *g*

g   *g*   *g*   *g*   *g*

gg   *gg*   *gg*   *gg*

gi

gip

fuzz

jazz

qu   *qu*   *qu*   *qu*

qu   *qu*   *qu*   *qu*

quit

quiz

quilt

quest

squid

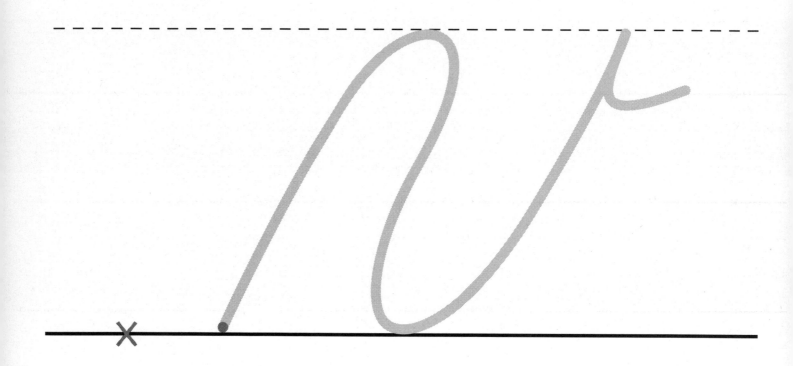

v v v v v

v v v v v

va

vi

ve

vat

vim

have

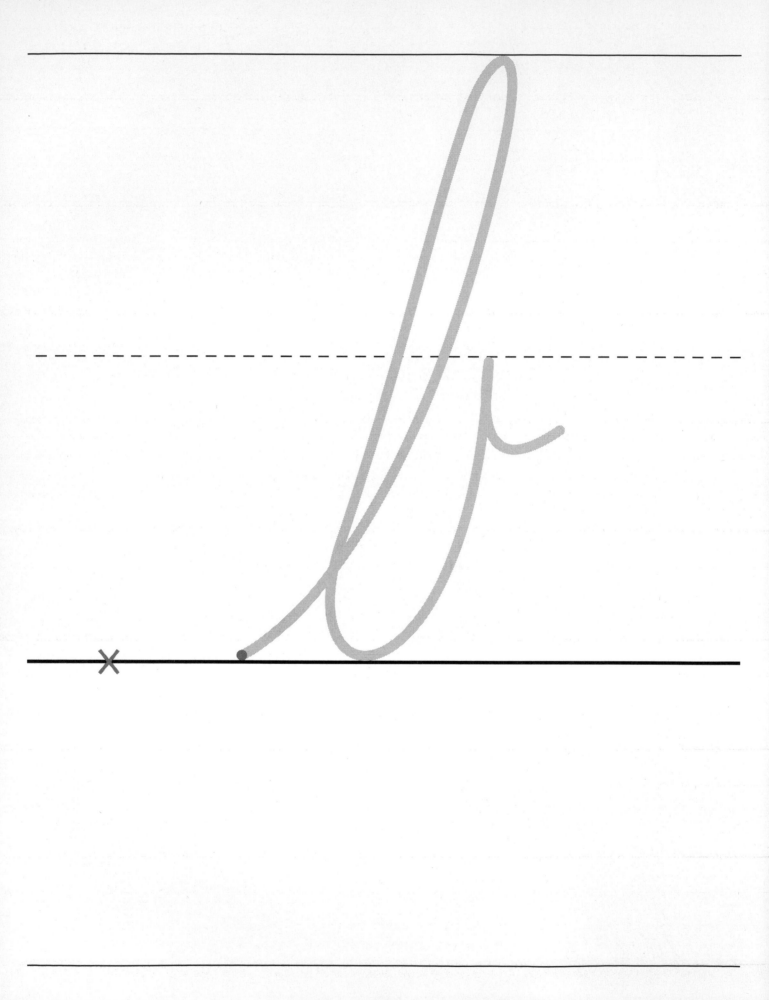

b   *b*   *b*   *b*   *b*

b   *b*   *b*   *b*   *b*

ba

bi

be

bu

bt

baby

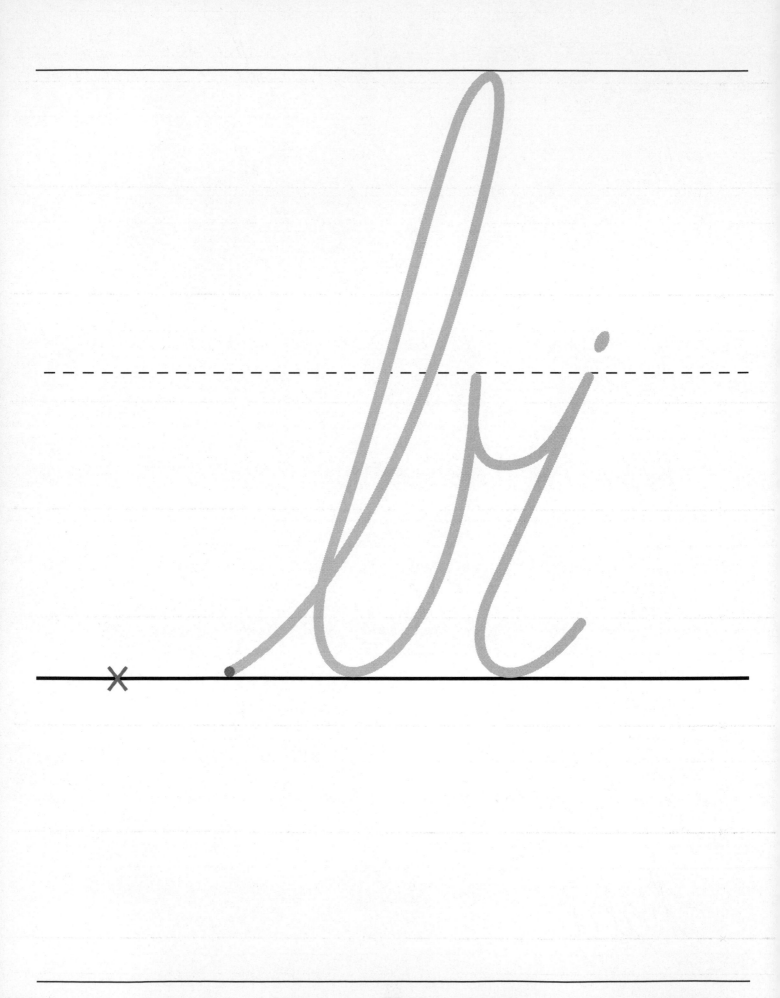

bi   bi   bi   bi   bi

bi   bi   bi   bi   bi

big

bit

bib

bill

cabin

habit

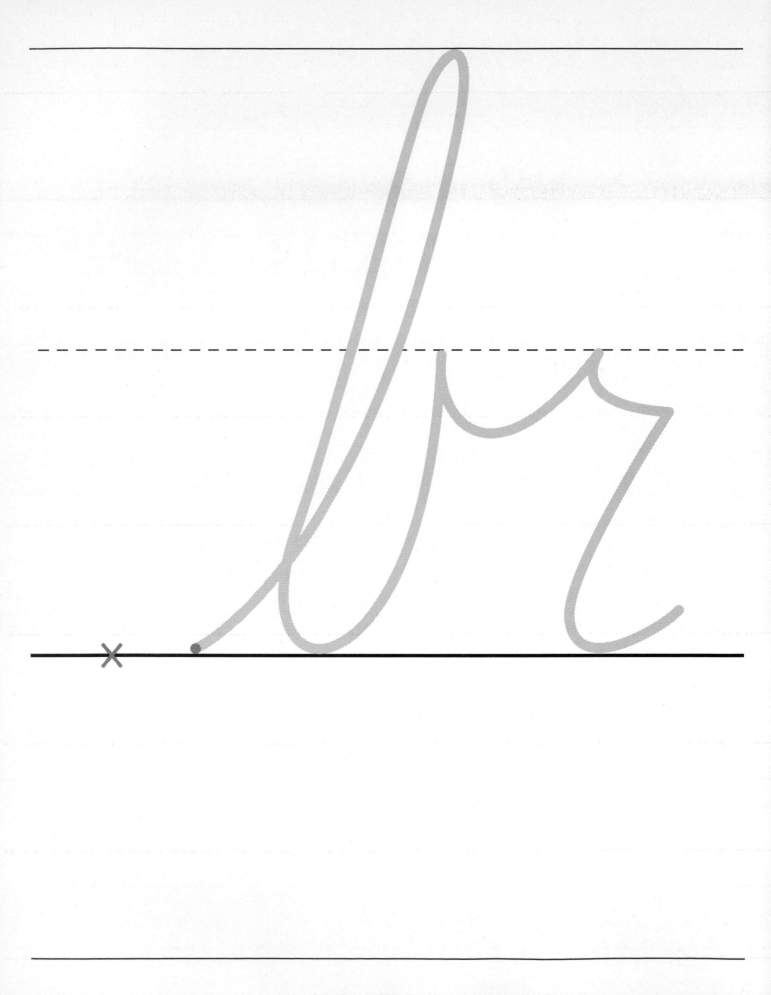

br   br   br   br

br   br   br   br

brat

bran

brag

brick

bring

brush

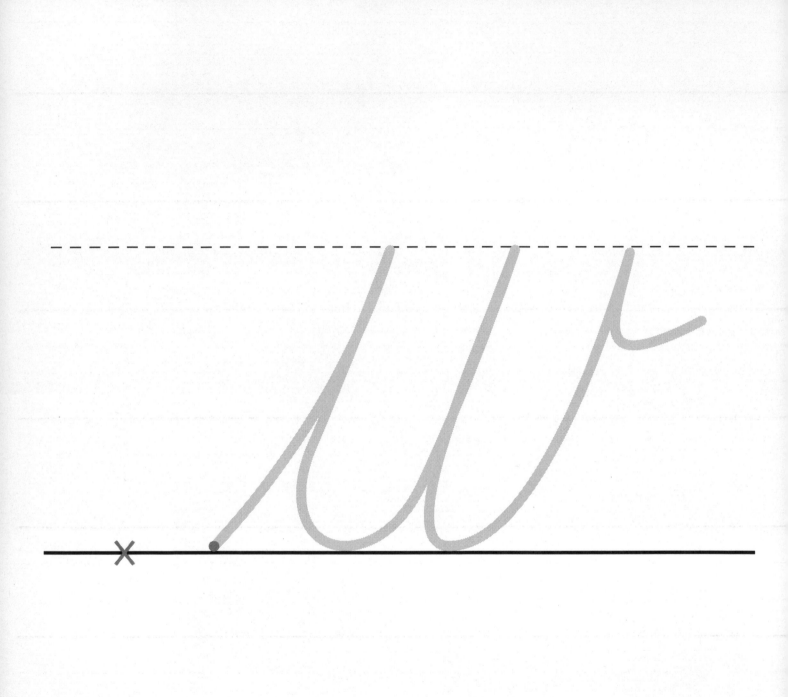

w w w w w

w w w w w

we

wet

wa

was

wi

will

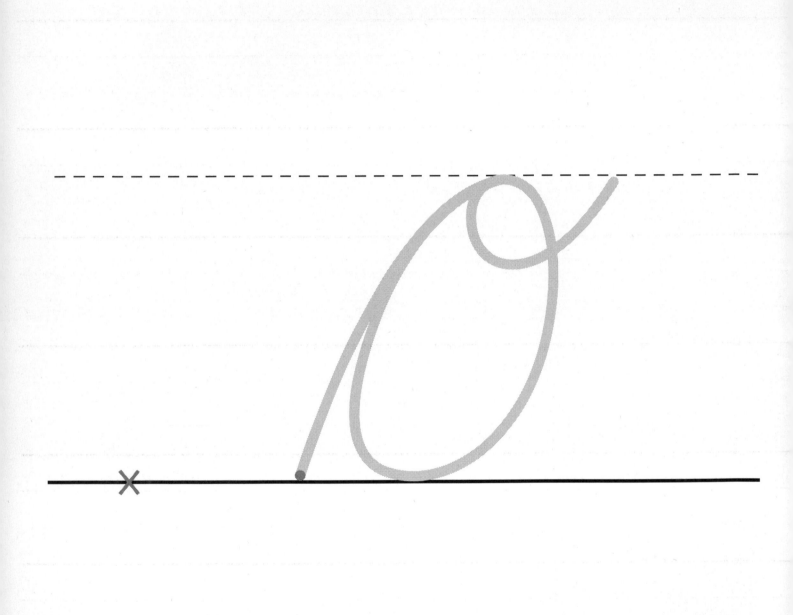

O   O   O   O   O

O   O   O   O   O

oo

oa

or

ow

op

ob

got

jog

for

hop

you

zoo

box

love

sobs

on   on   on   on

1 2

om   om   om   om

1 2 3

one

mom

long

prom

pond

65

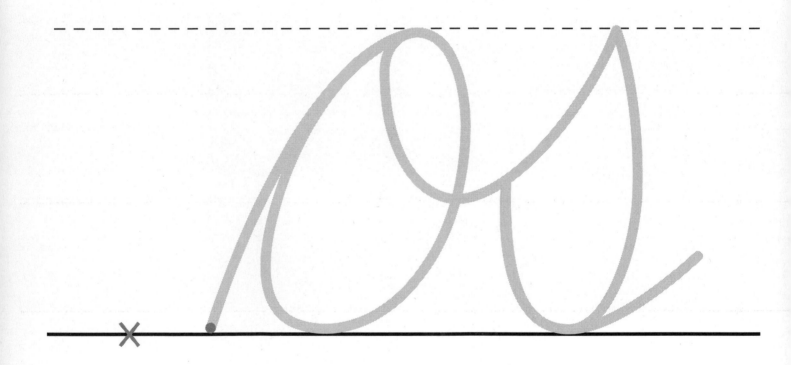

oo   oo   oo   oo   oo

oo   oo   oo   oo   oo

boss

toss

loss

moss

cross

c   cc

a   ca

ac

d   dd

ad   da

q   qq

qa   aq

dad

qaq

add

cad

Tall Letters

l   ll

l   ll

le   el

h   he

k   lk

f   ff

fe   ff

b   bl

be   ba

leg

had

fell

back

69

i	*u*
t	*it*
ut	*tu*
p	*pp*
up	*pi*
r	*ri*
s	*ss*
j	*ju*
w	*wh*
wa	*aw*
wi	*we*

rip

jet

wig

rut

wet

kiss

just

with

ship

pass

such

sick

n	*an*
in	*en*
m	*am*
im	*em*
y	*ye*
my	*my*
j	*ji*
jj	*jj*
v	*ve*
vy	*vi*
x	*ax*
ex	*ix*

man

vim

yes

zip

wax

men

jazz

give

have

name

mixing

buzzing

qu

quit

quilt

squid

o   oo

oa   ow

ob   ox

lot

fox

dogs

hopping

stocking

on

one

pond

long

om

mom

prom

from

blond

come

strong

lemon

a a a a a

a a a a a

Ann

Amy

Atlantic

Alaska

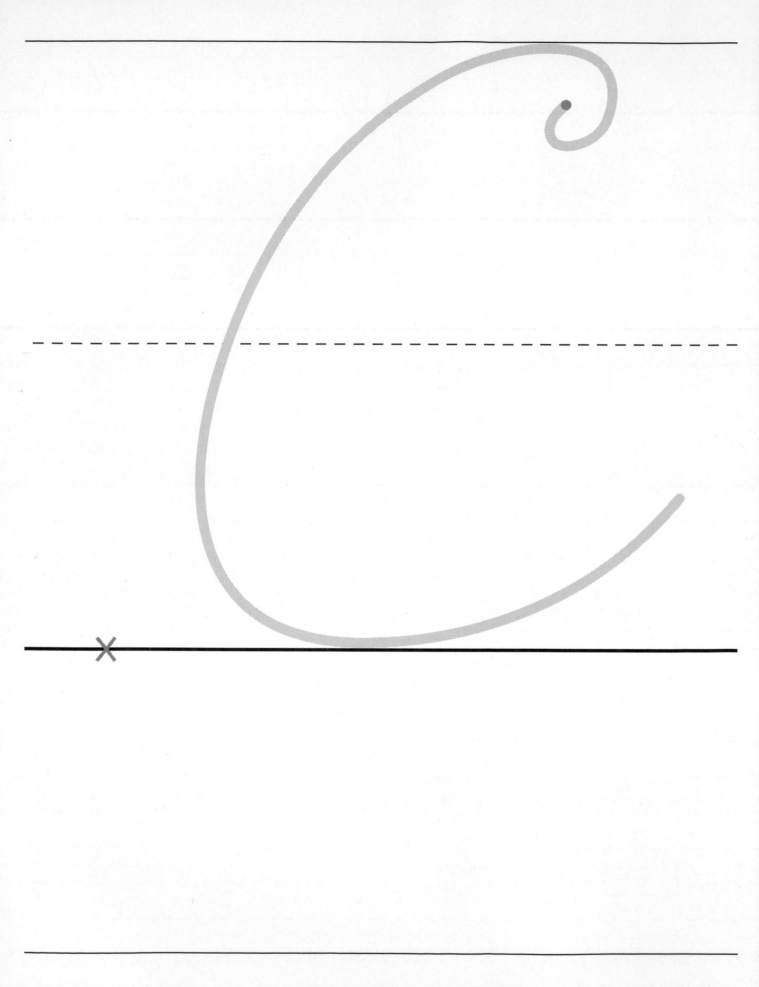

C   C   C   C   C   C

C   C   C   C   C

Carl

Clark

Columbus

Canada

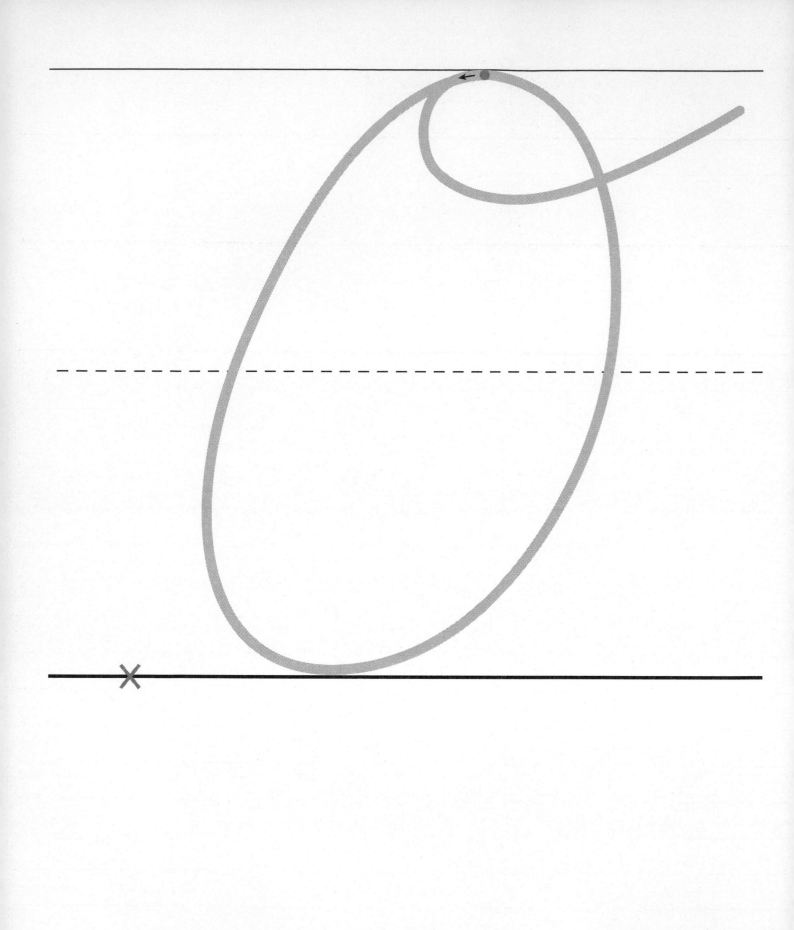

Oh!

October

Oliver

Ohio

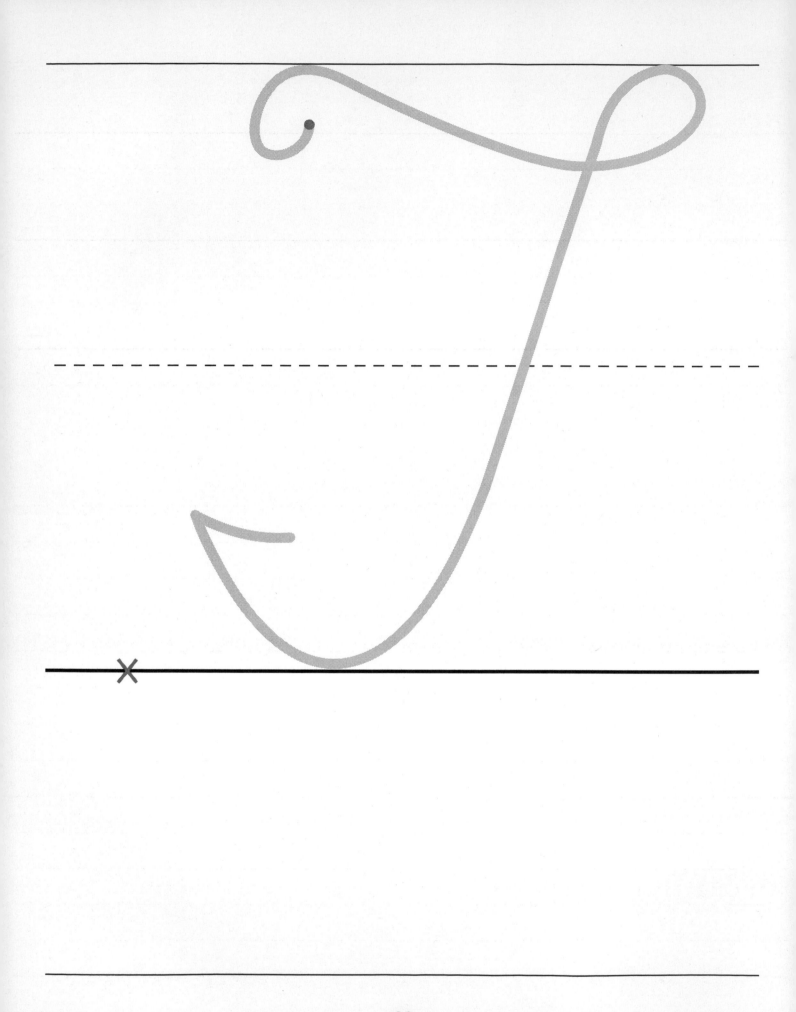

T *T* *T* *T* *T*

T *T* *T* *T* *T*

Tom

Tim

Ted

Texas

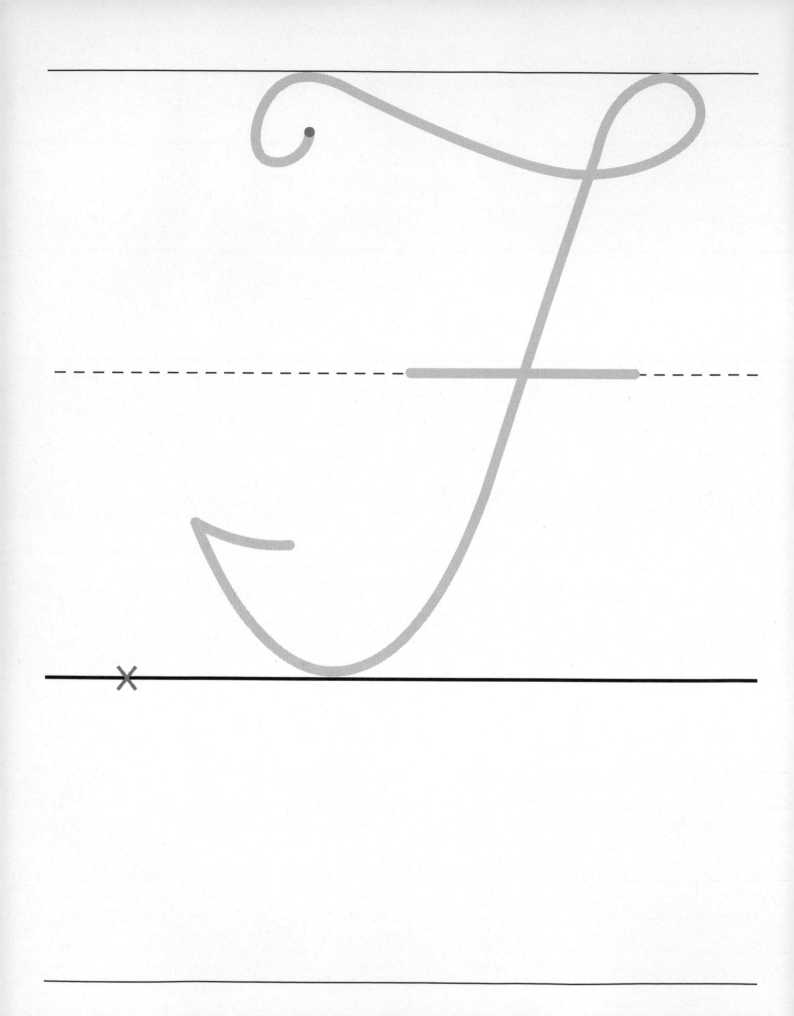

$\mathcal{F}$ $\mathcal{F}$ $\mathcal{F}$ $\mathcal{F}$ $\mathcal{F}$

$\mathcal{F}$ $\mathcal{F}$ $\mathcal{F}$ $\mathcal{F}$ $\mathcal{F}$

Fran

Fred

Felix

Friday

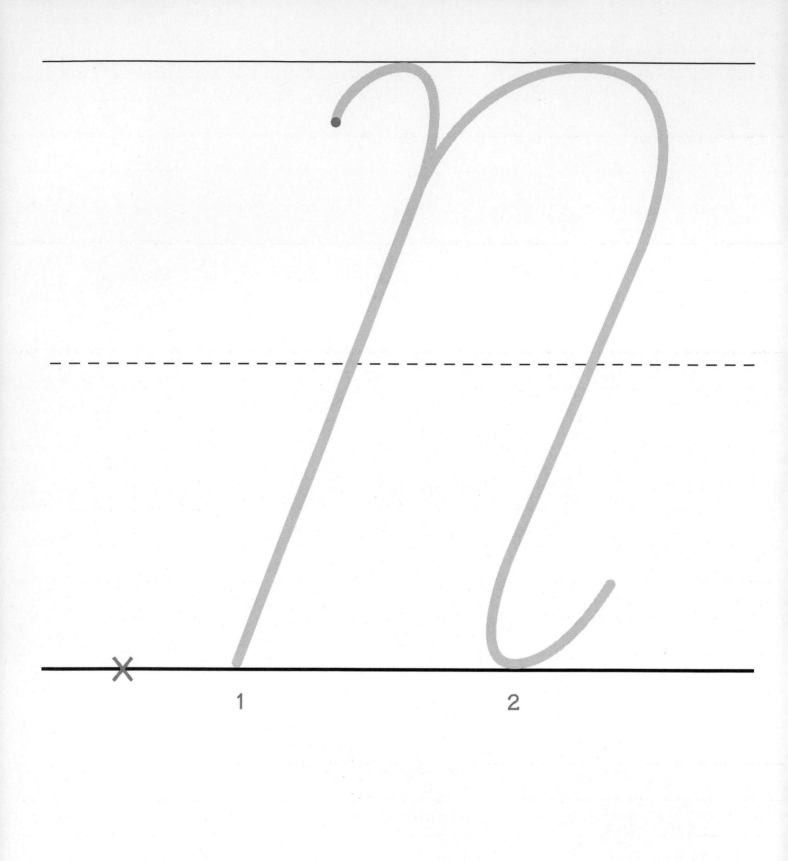

1   2

n n n n n

1   2

n n n n n

1   2

Nat

Ned

Nan

November

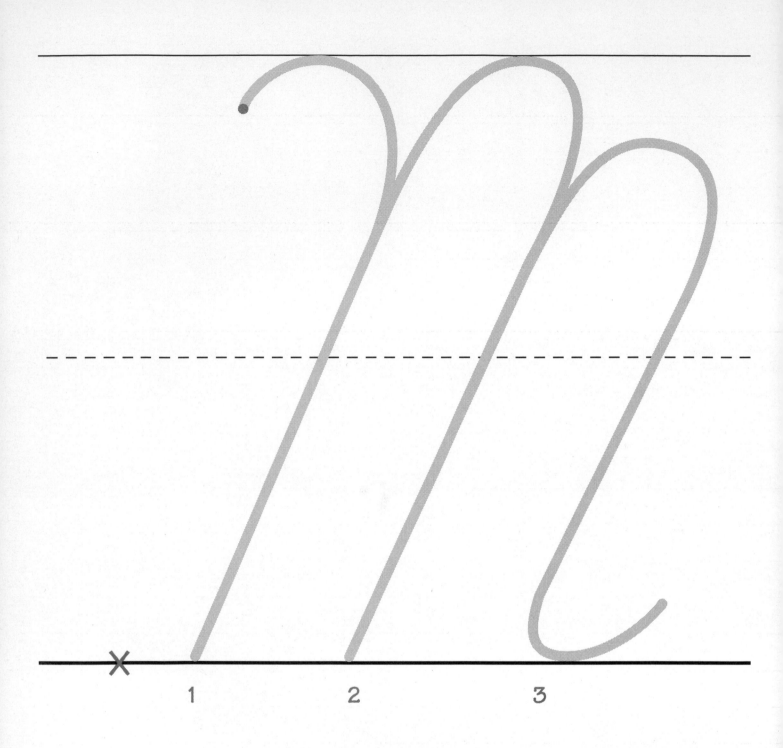

1   2   3

$\mathcal{M}$ $\mathcal{M}$ $\mathcal{M}$ $\mathcal{M}$ $\mathcal{M}$

1 2 3

$\mathcal{M}$ $\mathcal{M}$ $\mathcal{M}$ $\mathcal{M}$ $\mathcal{M}$

1 2 3

Mr.

Mrs.

Ms.

Miss

$\mathcal{H}$ $\mathcal{H}$ $\mathcal{H}$ $\mathcal{H}$ $\mathcal{H}$

$\mathcal{H}$ $\mathcal{H}$ $\mathcal{H}$ $\mathcal{H}$ $\mathcal{H}$

Hal

Hank

Hudson

Halloween

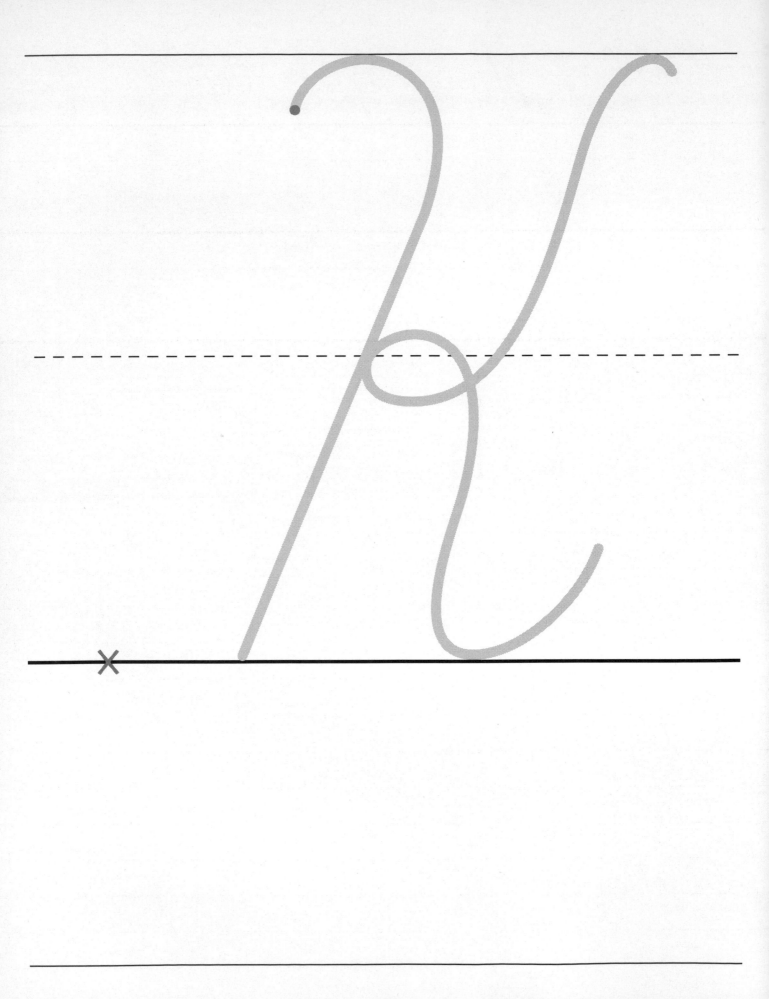

$\mathcal{K}$ $\mathcal{K}$ $\mathcal{K}$ $\mathcal{K}$ $\mathcal{K}$

$\mathcal{K}$ $\mathcal{K}$ $\mathcal{K}$ $\mathcal{K}$ $\mathcal{K}$

Kim

Ken

Kevin

OK

P   P   P   P   P

P   P   P   P   P

Pam

Peg

Pat

Pluto

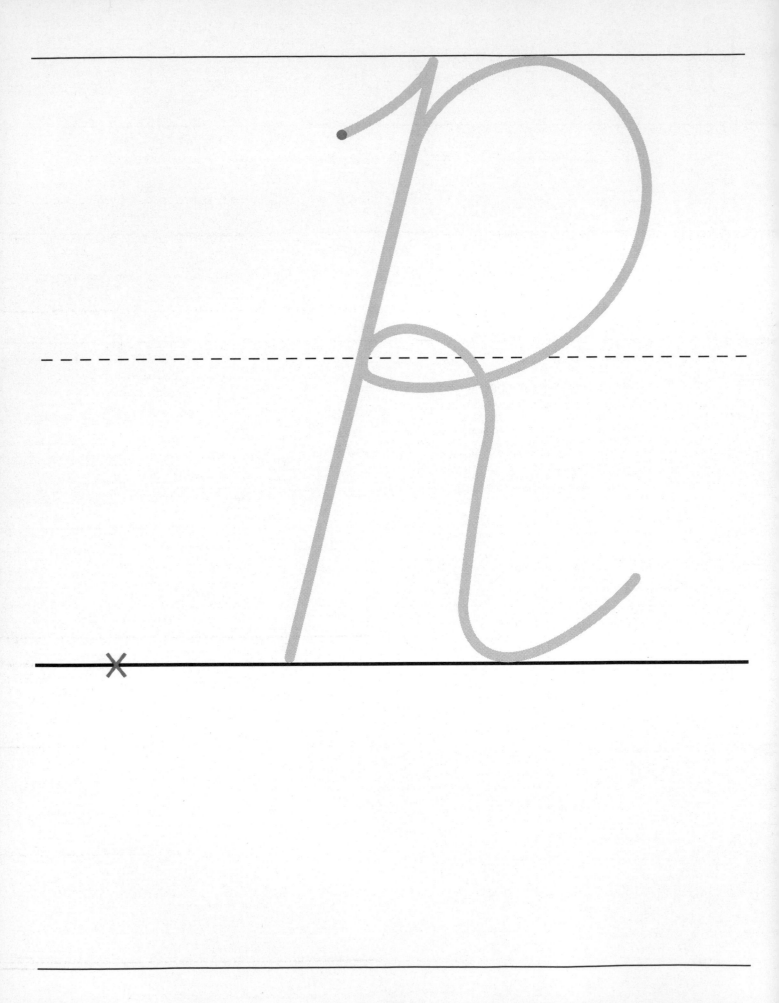

$\mathcal{R}$ $\mathcal{R}$ $\mathcal{R}$ $\mathcal{R}$ $\mathcal{R}$

$\mathcal{R}$ $\mathcal{R}$ $\mathcal{R}$ $\mathcal{R}$ $\mathcal{R}$

Rick

Robin

Reno

Red River

B B B B B

B B B B B

Bob

Beth

Bronx

Boston

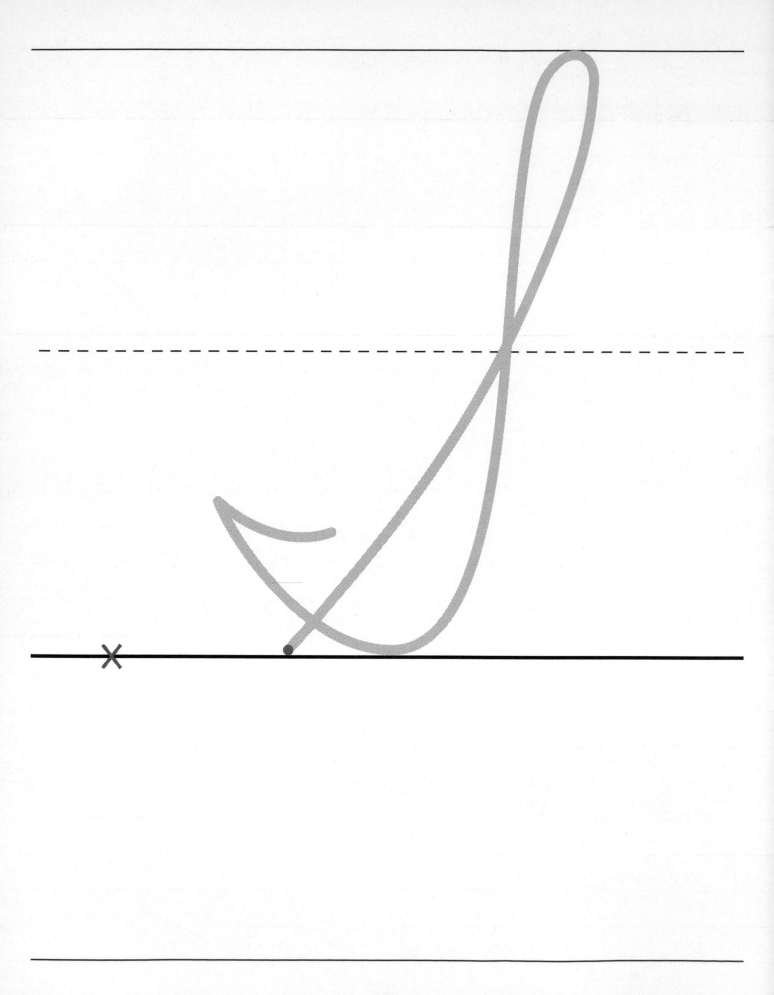

$\mathcal{S}$ $\mathcal{S}$ $\mathcal{S}$ $\mathcal{S}$ $\mathcal{S}$

$\mathcal{S}$ $\mathcal{S}$ $\mathcal{S}$ $\mathcal{S}$ $\mathcal{S}$

Sam

Sid

Sunday

September

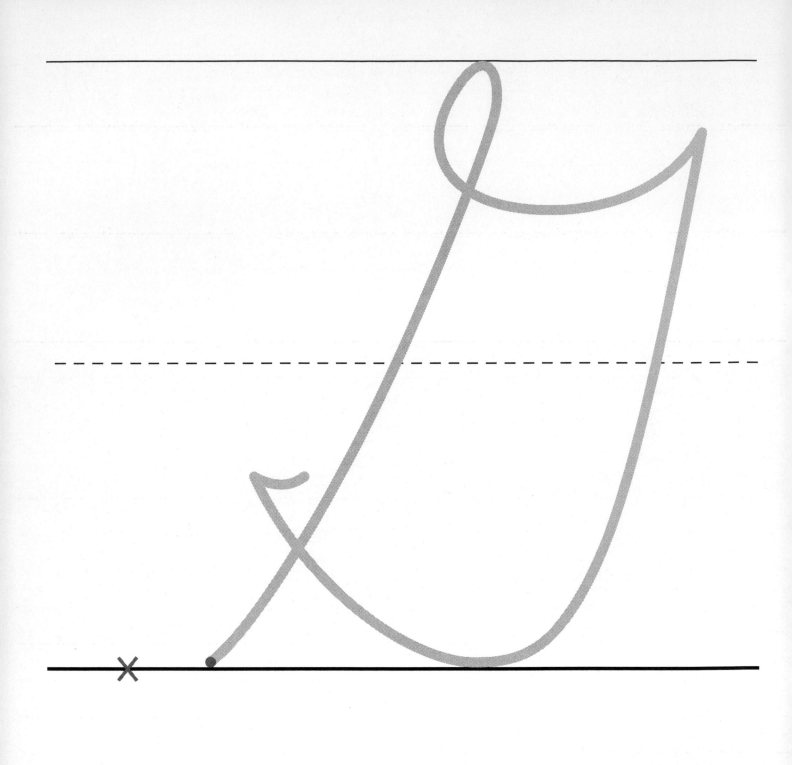

$\mathscr{G}$ $\mathscr{G}$ $\mathscr{G}$ $\mathscr{G}$ $\mathscr{G}$

$\mathscr{G}$ $\mathscr{G}$ $\mathscr{G}$ $\mathscr{G}$ $\mathscr{G}$

Gus

Glen

Greg

Gwen

l   *l*   *l*   *l*   *l*

l   *l*   *l*   *l*   *l*

I'm

I'll

Iran

Idaho

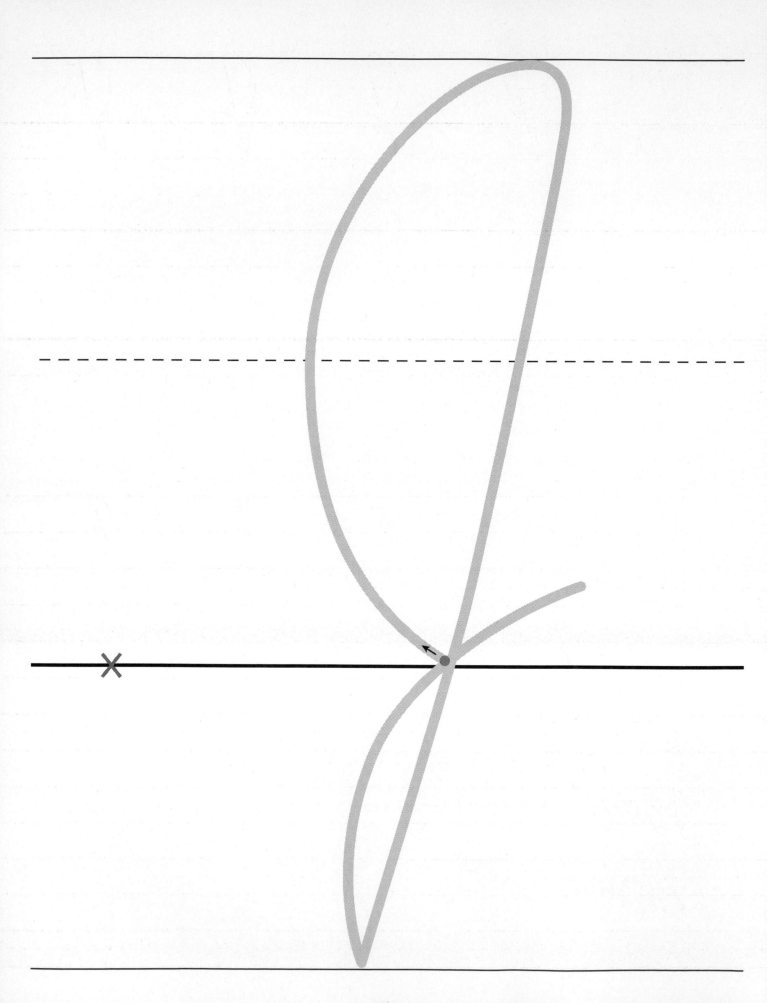

$\mathcal{J}$ $\mathcal{J}$ $\mathcal{J}$ $\mathcal{J}$ $\mathcal{J}$

$\mathcal{J}$ $\mathcal{J}$ $\mathcal{J}$ $\mathcal{J}$ $\mathcal{J}$

Jack

Jill

Jupiter

Jefferson

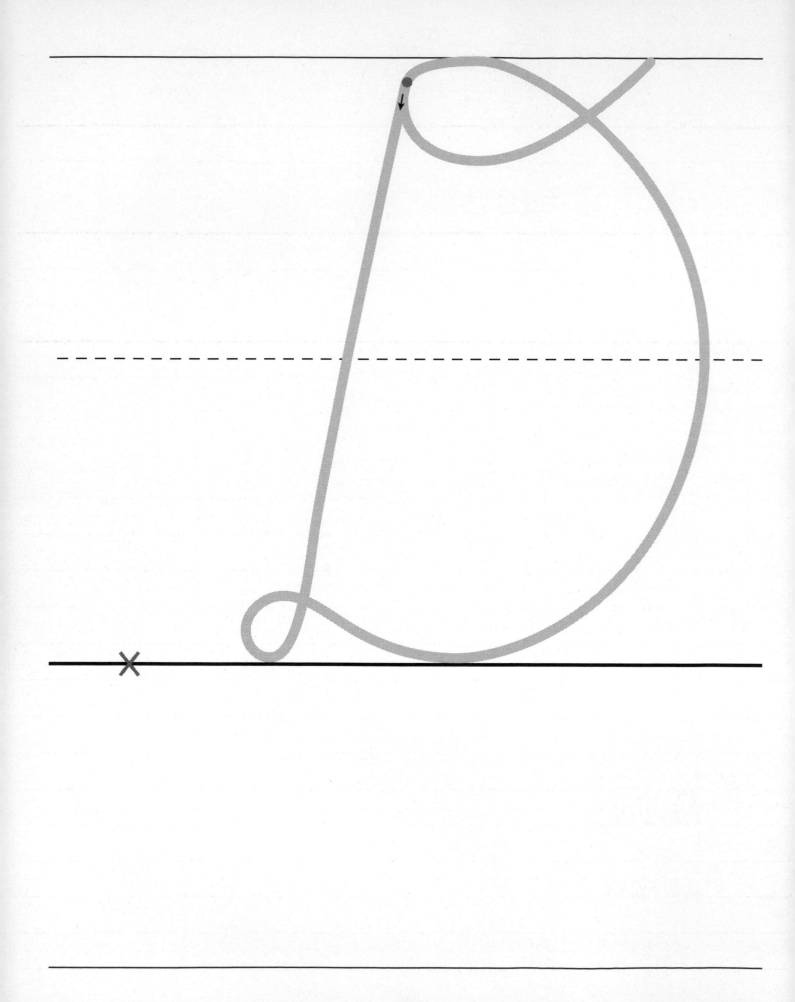

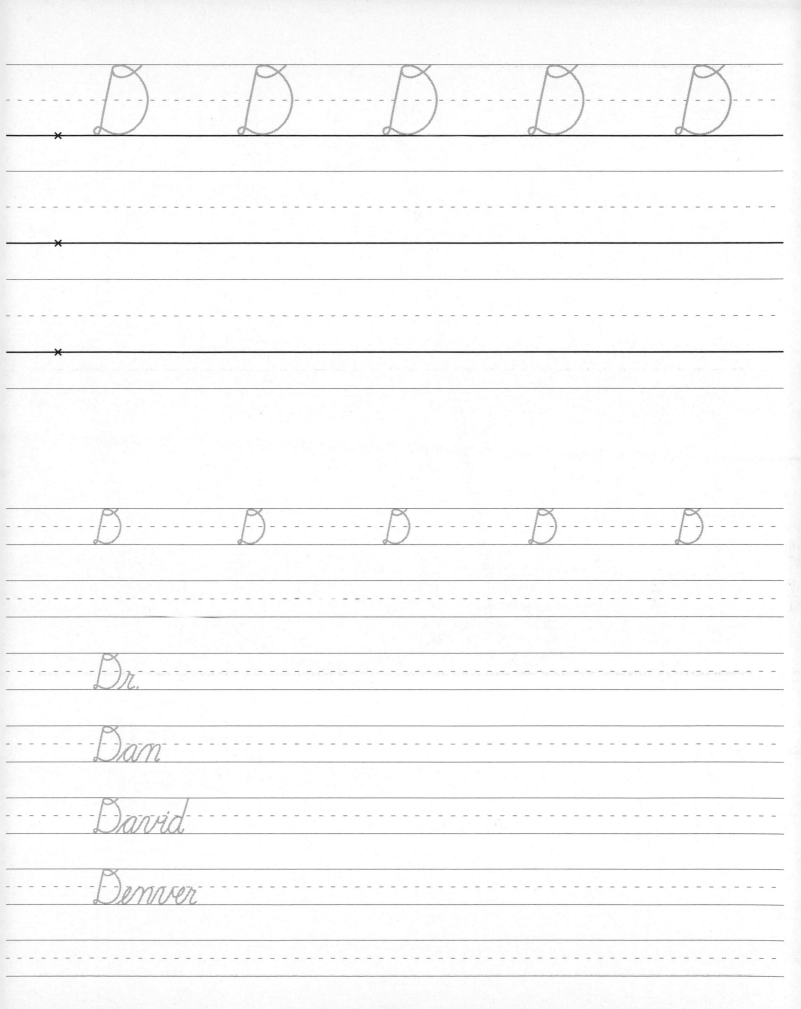

Dr.

Dan

David

Denver

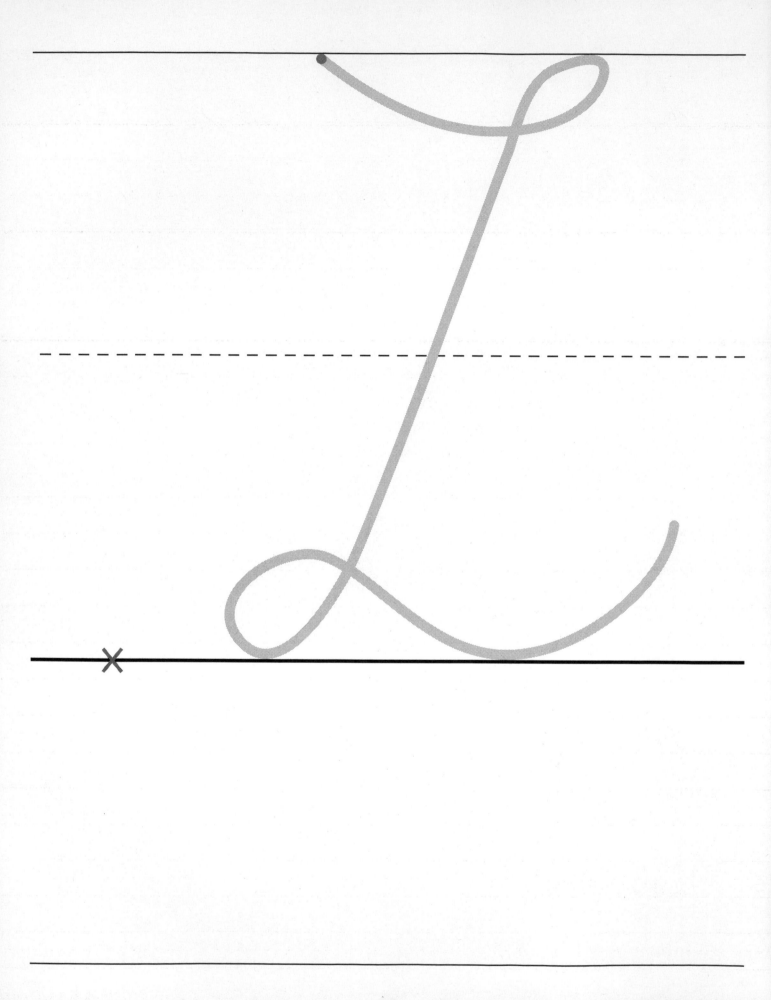

$\mathcal{L}$ $\mathcal{L}$ $\mathcal{L}$ $\mathcal{L}$ $\mathcal{L}$

$\mathcal{L}$ $\mathcal{L}$ $\mathcal{L}$ $\mathcal{L}$ $\mathcal{L}$

Lil

Len

Linda

Lexington

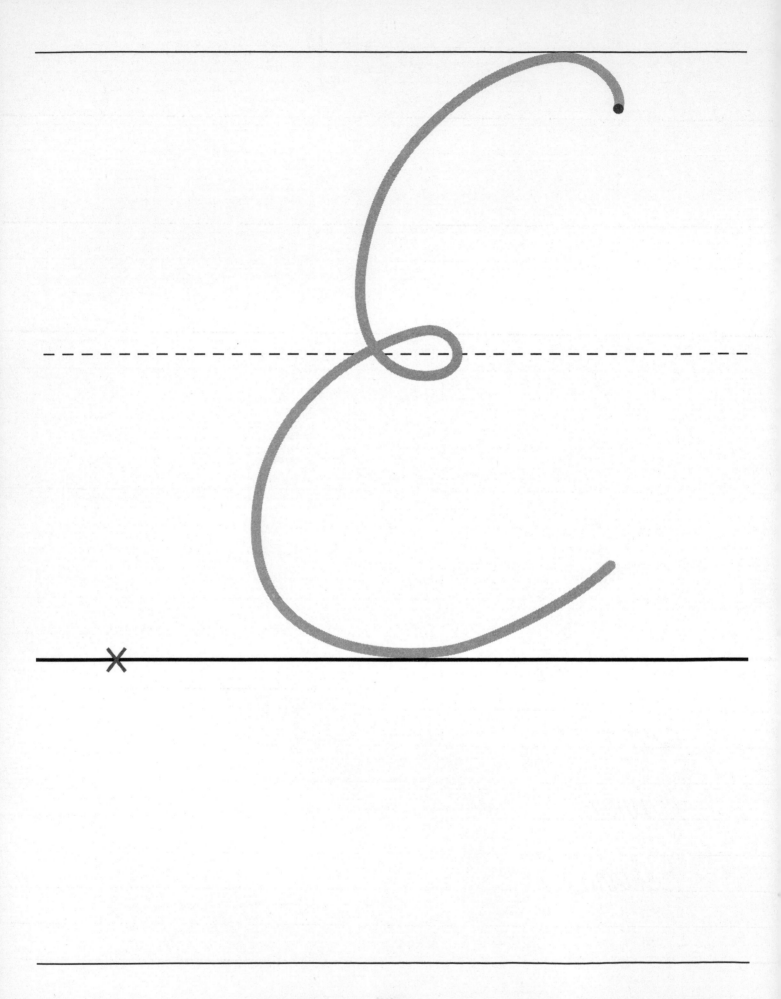

$\mathcal{E}$ $\mathcal{E}$ $\mathcal{E}$ $\mathcal{E}$ $\mathcal{E}$

$\mathcal{E}$ $\mathcal{E}$ $\mathcal{E}$ $\mathcal{E}$ $\mathcal{E}$

Ed

Evan

Edwin

Eskimo

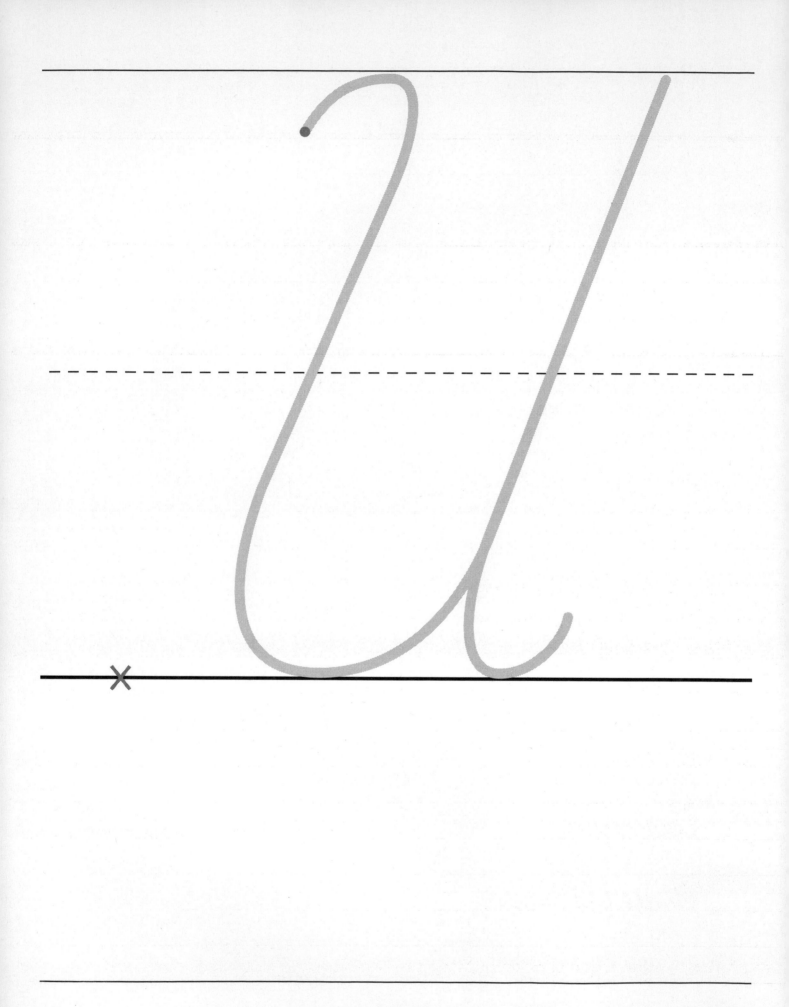

U *U* *U* *U* *U*

U *U* *U* *U* *U*

USA

UFO

Uranus

United States

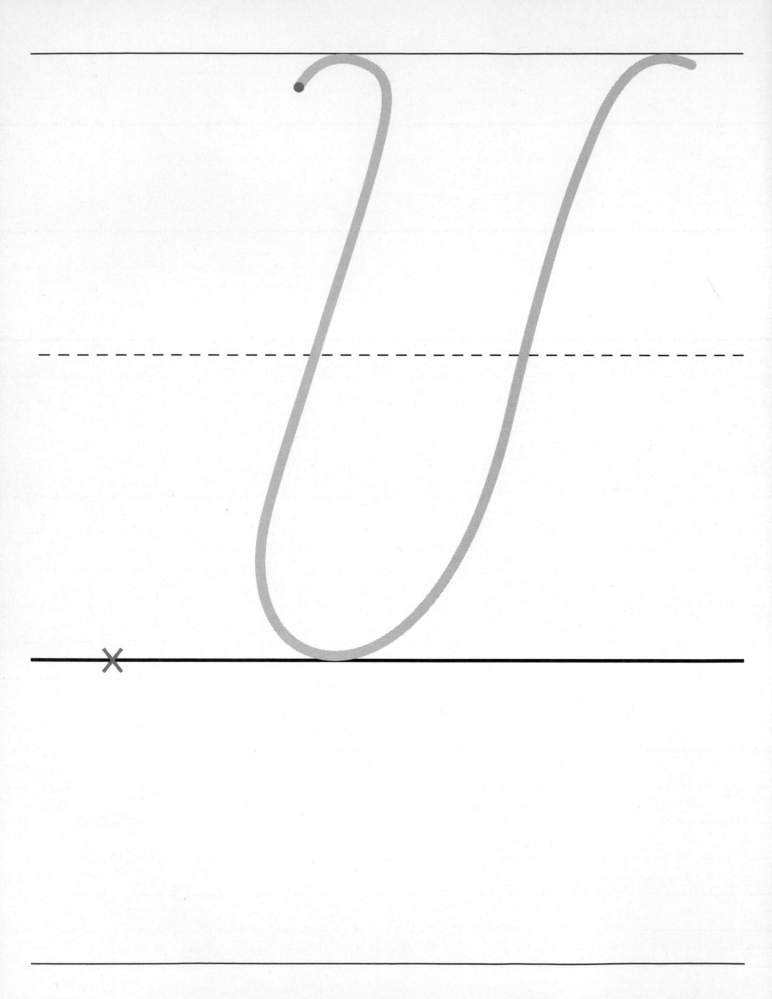

$\mathcal{U}$ $\mathcal{U}$ $\mathcal{U}$ $\mathcal{U}$ $\mathcal{U}$

$\mathcal{U}$ $\mathcal{U}$ $\mathcal{U}$ $\mathcal{U}$ $\mathcal{U}$

V

Vic

Venus

Vermont

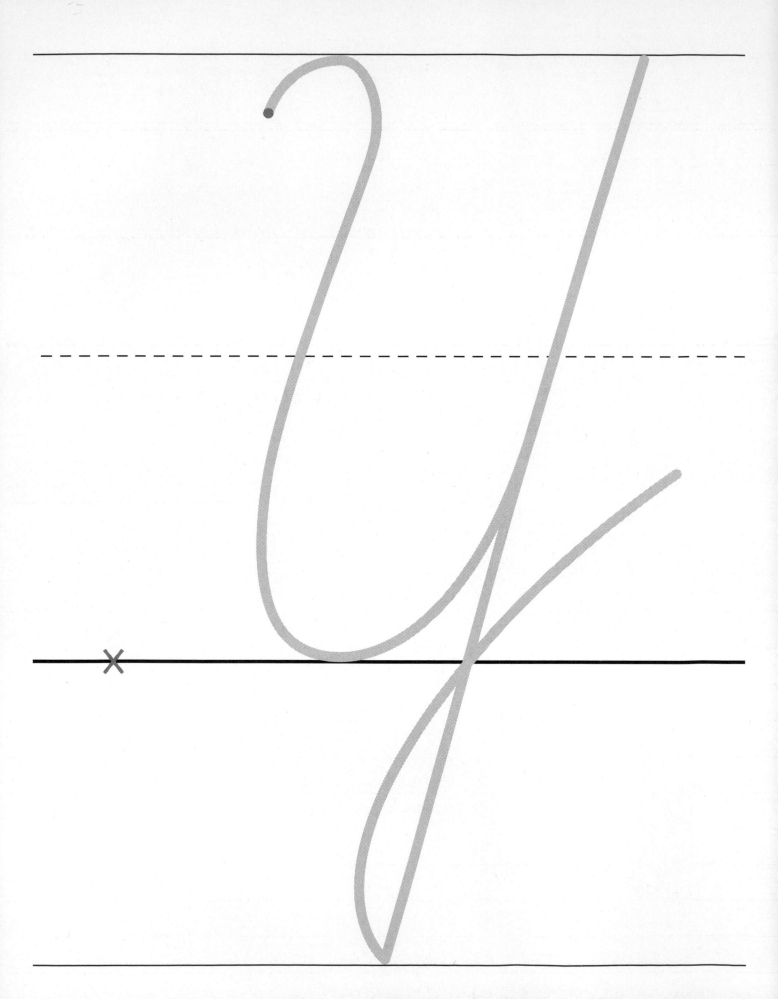

$\mathcal{Y}$ $\mathcal{Y}$ $\mathcal{Y}$ $\mathcal{Y}$ $\mathcal{Y}$

$\mathcal{Y}$ $\mathcal{Y}$ $\mathcal{Y}$ $\mathcal{Y}$ $\mathcal{Y}$

YMCA

Yes!

NY

York

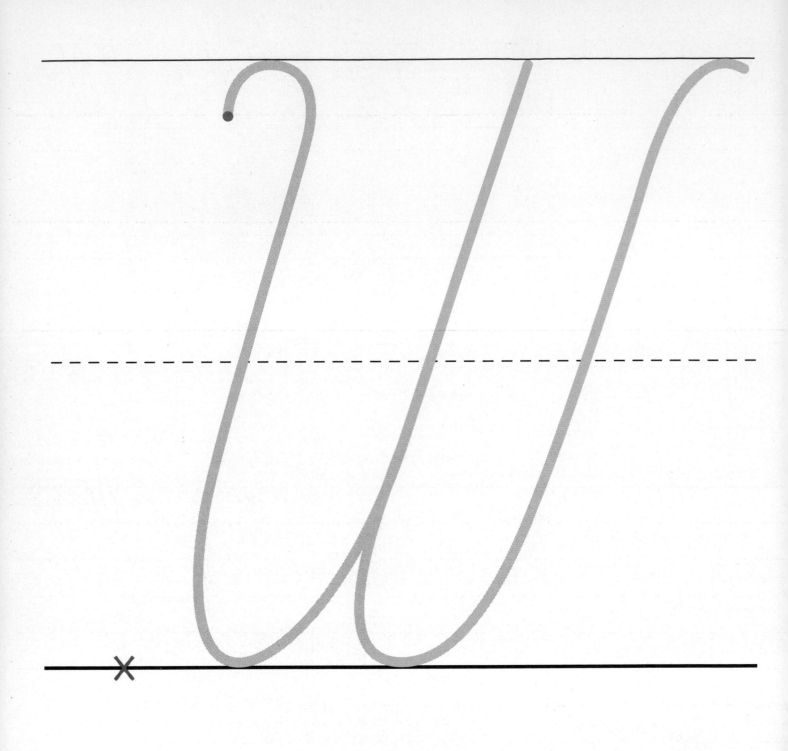

$\mathcal{U}$ $\mathcal{U}$ $\mathcal{U}$ $\mathcal{U}$ $\mathcal{U}$

$\mathcal{U}$ $\mathcal{U}$ $\mathcal{U}$ $\mathcal{U}$ $\mathcal{U}$

Wilt

Winston

Wisconsin

Washington, D.C.

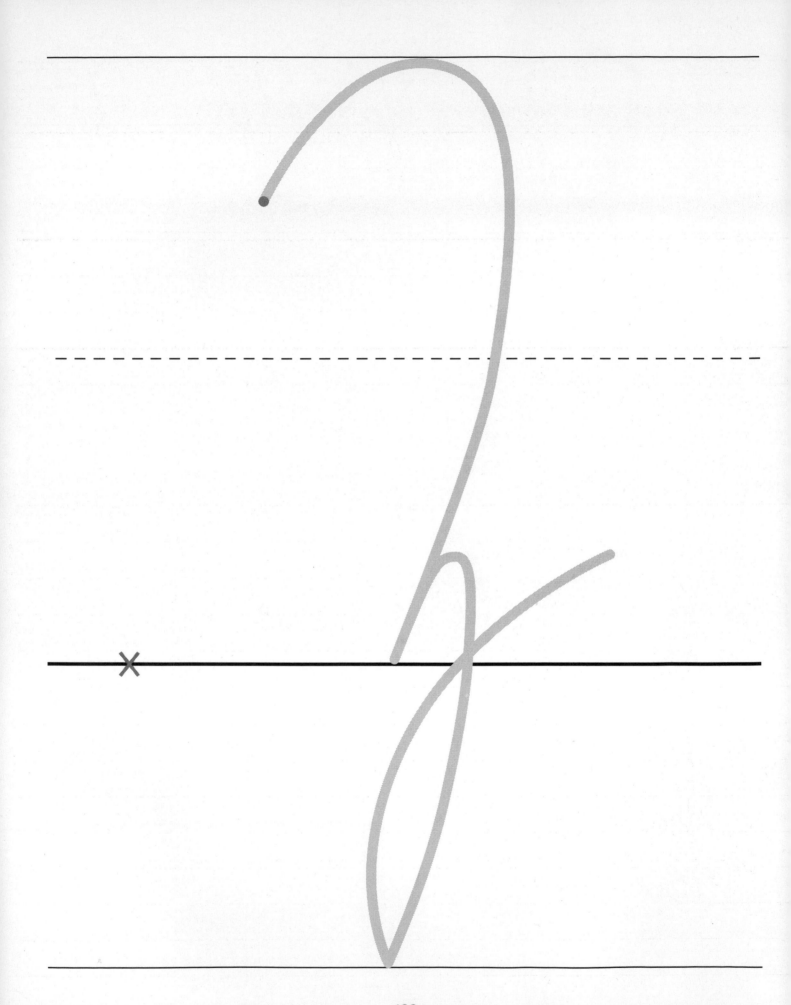

Zed

Zack

Zulu

Bronx Zoo

123

Qu   *Qu*   *Qu*   *Qu*

Qu   *Qu*   *Qu*   *Qu*

Quentin

Quaker

Quiet!

Quebec

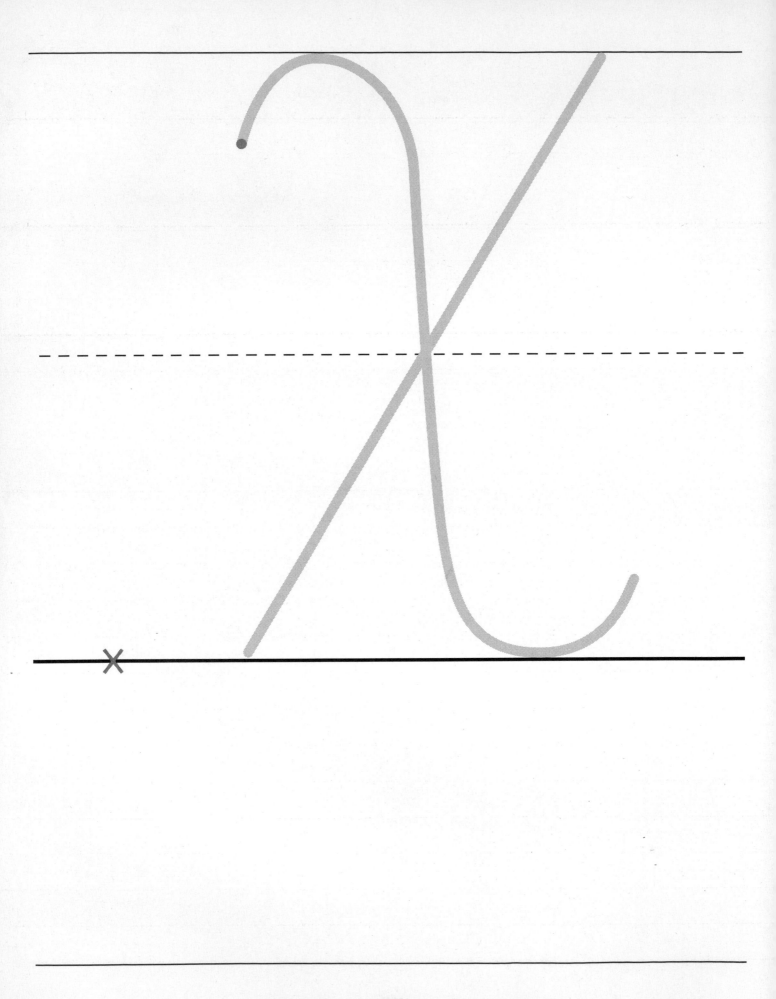